MANY MESSAGES

SENIOR AUTHORS

Virginia A. Arnold   Carl B. Smith

AUTHORS

James Flood   Diane Lapp

LITERATURE CONSULTANTS

Joan I. Glazer   Margaret H. Lippert

Macmillan Publishing Company
New York

Collier Macmillan Publishers
London

Parts of this work were published in the first edition of CONNECTIONS.
This work is also published together with other works in a single volume under the title *BIT BY BIT*, copyright © 1989 Macmillan Publishing Company, a division of Macmillan, Inc.

Macmillan Publishing Company
866 Third Avenue
New York, N.Y. 10022
Collier Macmillan Canada, Inc.

Printed in the United States of America.

ISBN 0-02-175000-9

9 8 7 6 5 4 3

ACKNOWLEDGMENTS

The publisher gratefully acknowledges permission to reprint the following copyrighted material:

"Alexander Calder: Just For the Fun of It" by Gail Tuchman ". . . so I made a circus just for the fun of it . . ." comes from THE ARTIST'S VOICE: "Talks with Seventeen Artists" by Katharine Kuh. Copyright © 1960, 1961, 1962 by Katharine Kuh. Used by permission of Harper & Row, Publishers, Inc. "I want to make things that are fun to look at." From CONVERSATIONS WITH ARTISTS by Selden Rodman. Copyright © 1957 by Selden Rodman. Published by The Devin-Adair Company and used with their permission.

"Best Wishes, Ed" (text only) from WINSTON, NEWTON, ELTON, AND ED by James Stevenson. Copyright © 1978 by James Stevenson. Adapted by permission of Greenwillow Books (A Division of William Morrow & Company).

"Gloria Who Might Be My Best Friend" is an adaptation of text only from pp. 58-71 of THE STORIES JULIAN TELLS by Ann Cameron. Copyright © 1981 by Ann Cameron. Adapted by permission of Pantheon Books, a division of Random House, Inc.

"I'm up here" is Poem #13 from ANY ME I WANT TO BE, Poems by Karla Kuskin. Copyright © 1972 by Karla Kuskin. All rights reserved. Reprinted by permission of Harper & Row, Publishers, Inc.

"My Other Name" from A SONG I SANG TO YOU by Myra Cohn Livingston. Copyright © 1984, 1969, 1967, 1965, 1959, 1958 by Myra Cohn Livingston. All rights reserved. Reprinted by permission of Marian Reiner for the author.

"Reading" from RHYMES ABOUT US by Marchette Chute. Copyright © 1974 by Marchette Chute. Reprinted by permission of the publisher, E. P. Dutton, a division of New American Library and by permission of the author.

"So Will I" from RIVER WINDING by Charlotte Zolotow (Thomas Y. Crowell). Text copyright © 1970 by Charlotte Zolotow. Reprinted by permission of Harper & Row, Publishers, Inc. and World's Work Windmill Press.

"Through Grandpa's Eyes" is an abridged and adapted selection with 6 illustrations from THROUGH GRANDPA'S EYES by Patricia MacLachlan. Pictures by Deborah Ray. Text copyright © 1979 by Patricia MacLachlan. Illustrations copyright © 1980 by Deborah Ray. Reprinted by permission of Harper & Row, Publishers, Inc. and Curtis Brown Ltd.

Cover Design: John Sanford

Feature Logos and Medallion Logos: Eva Vagreti Cockrille

Unit Opener: Bob Shein

ILLUSTRATION CREDITS: Sal Murdocca, 4–8; Debbie Pinkney, 10–18; Patti Boyd, 22–32; Bob Shein, 34–35; Janet Bohn, 44, 45, 114, 115, 137–152; Sally Springer, 46–54; Ellen Appleby, 56–57; Carlos Freire, 58–68; Jan Pyk, 71; Karen Loccisano, 72–79; Bob Radigan, 81; Elliot Kreloff, 82–90; Allan Eitzen, 94–102; Patricia Henderson Lincoln, 134–135.

PHOTO CREDITS: © Peggy Jarrell Kaplan, 70. MAGNUM PHOTOS: © Inge Morath, 116. © Blair Seitz, 36 to 42. Collection of WHITNEY MUSEUM OF AMERICAN ART: 116–122. Alexander Calder. *Chock.* (1972). Metal assemblage. 11x28x22 inches. Gift of the artist. Acq. #72.55, 117; *Kangaroo* from the *Circus.* (1926–31). Metal, wood and wire. 5½x8x3¼ inches. Acq. #83.36.6, 118B; *Clown* from the *Circus.* (1926–31). Wire, painted wood, cloth, yarn, leather, metal and button. 10½x9x4 inches. Acq. #83.36.3, 120TL; *Lion and Cage* from the *Circus.* (1926–31). Wire, yarn, cloth and buttons. 9½x16½x5 inches. (lion). Painted wood, wire, cloth, cork and bottle caps. 17⅛x19½x17½ inches. (cage). Acq. #83.36a-b, 120TR; *Seals* from the *Circus.* (1926–31). Painted wood, metal, wire, cork and platic ball. 8x19⅝x5 inches. Acq. #83.36.10, 120B; *Big Bug.* 1970. Gouache on paper. 29⅛x42¾ inches. Promised gift of Howard and Jean Lipman. Acq. #P.40.80, 121. © Allen Yarinsky, 122. Collection of Nanette Hayes Saxton, Alexander Calder. *Circus,* 1926, oil on burlap, 69x83 inches. On extended loan to University Art Museum, Berkeley, California, 118T. Collection of WHITNEY MUSEUM OF AMERICAN ART: Purchased with funds from a public fundraising campaign in May 1982. One half the funds were contributed by the Robert Wood Johnson Jr. Charitable Trust. Additional major donations were given by The Lauder Foundation; the Robert Lehman Foundation, Inc.; the Howard and Jean Lipman Foundation, Inc.; an anonymous donor; The T.M. Evans Foundation, Inc.; MacAndrews & Forbes Group, Incorporated; the De Witt Wallace Fund; Martin and Agneta Gruss; Anne Phillips; Mr. and Mrs. Laurence S. Rockefeller; the Simon Foundation, Inc.; Marylou Whitney; Bankers Trust Company; Mr. and Mrs. Kenneth N. Dayton; Joel and Anne Ehrenkranz; Irvin and Kenneth Feld; Flora Whitney Miller. More than 500 individuals from 26 states and abroad also contributed to the campaign. 83.86, 118B, 120.

Contents

Introducing Level 6, Unit 1 *MANY MESSAGES* _____ **9**

The Code Toad, *a mystery story*
by Carol Carrick _____ **10**

SKILLS ACTIVITY: Sequence of Events _____ **20**

I Don't Like Reading, *a fantasy*
by Virginia Arnold _____ **22**

Reading, *a poem by Marchette Chute* _____ **34**

At the Library, *a photo-essay*
by Marlyn Mangus _____ **36**

SKILLS ACTIVITY: Recall Details —————— **44**

The Name Day, *a story by Gibbs Davis* —————— **46**

 **My Other Name,** *a poem*
by Myra Cohn Livingston —————— **56**

Rumpelstiltskin, *a play based on*
the folk tale and retold by Margaret H. Lippert —— **58**

MEET THE AUTHOR: Margaret H. Lippert. —————— **70**

LANGUAGE ACTIVITY: Time for a Rhyme —————— **71**

6

Gloria Who Might Be My Best Friend, *a story by Anne Cameron* —————— **72**

I'm Up Here, *a poem by Karla Kuskin* —————— **81**

A Kite of Your Own, *a how-to selection by Loretta Kaim* —————— **82**

WRITING ACTIVITY: Story —————— **92**

I Wish I Were Back Home, *a series of letters by Argentina Palacios* —————— **94**

Best Wishes, Ed, *a story by James Stevenson* —————— **104**

7

SKILLS ACTIVITY: Realism and Fantasy _____ **114**

Alexander Calder: "Just For the Fun of It" *photo story by Gail Tuchman* _____ **116**

Through Grandpa's Eyes, *a story by Patricia MacLachlan with illustrations by Deborah Kogan Ray* _____ **124**

So Will I, *a poem by Charlotte Zolotow* _____ **134**

Concluding Level 6, Unit 1 MANY MESSAGES _____ **136**

GLOSSARY _____ **137**

8

Introducing Level 6

MANY MESSAGES

The more that you read,
the more things you will know.
The more that you learn,
the more places you'll go.

Dr. Seuss

You send and get messages every day. Wave hello, tell someone your name, write a letter —all are messages. In this unit, you will read about finding messages in a secret code, a book, a name, a letter, the tail of a kite, and a piece of art. How can messages help people share and learn?

The Code Toad

A code is a kind of message. Tim finds that a code is a way to get to know new people. These new friends want to crack the code. Read to find out what a Code Toad is.

It was Tim's first day in his new school. Tim listened to the teacher call out every name. That was how he came to know that the boy who sat next to him was Scott. Tim looked at Scott. If he could have one wish, it would be to have Scott for a friend.

When the boys and girls went out to the playground, some of them had a soccer ball to kick. Scott and a boy called Jason picked nine players, but they didn't want Tim on their team.

"We don't need more players," they said. "We have all we want now."

Tim could play soccer. He was even very good at it, but they didn't let him show them. He hated to just watch.

Just before the game was over, the ball came Tim's way.

"Look out!" shouted Jason as he ran to stop the ball. Tim was in his way and Jason banged into him. Then they heard the teacher call out that it was time to go inside. The game was over. Because of Tim, it was a bad day for Jason.

It was a bad day for Tim, too. When he got on the bus to go home he walked by some of the boys from his room. No one asked him to sit with them. So he sat in the back and listened while they shouted to one another. Seeing them have so much fun, Tim felt sad inside. He hated this new school.

Tim walked home from the bus stop. His bag full of books felt so heavy. When he came inside, his mother asked, "Why do you look so sad?"

"Nobody would play with me in school," Tim told her. "They all have friends and they don't want to make a new one."

"It was your first day. Give them a little time to get to know you," his mother told him. "I know things will change."

"That isn't much help now," thought Tim. Tim sat down and began to read one of the books his grandmother gave him.

He sat on the creaking steps in front
of his house and read and read. The book
had a secret way to write called code.

There were all kinds. Tim began to try
them out. At first he could only say one
word in code at a time. He had to work at
it until he could say a full sentence in
code. Soon he could say anything he
wanted. It was like a game.

Before school the next day, he put a
secret message on Scott's chair. It said—

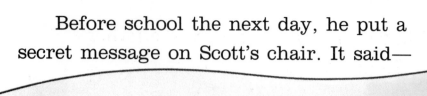

atchway utoay orfay hetay
iantgay odecay oadtay!

Seeing the message, Scott's friends
wanted to know what it said.

"It's in code, but I know how to read
it," Scott told them. "It says—**WATCH OUT
FOR THE GIANT CODE TOAD**."

"But who is this from?" asked a boy.

Scott said he still didn't know who it was.

That night Tim thought of another code. He had to stay up late to plan it. After he thought it all out he began to draw. It was like a crossword game.

**IF YOU CAN READ
THIS SECRET MESSAGE
YOU CAN BE A CODE TOAD.**

Before school the next day, Tim began to slide a new message on every chair in his room. When the boys and girls saw that the Code Toad was back again, they laughed.

15

"Is this some kind of a joke?" Jason asked Scott.

"I don't know," said Scott. "But this is fun. I would like to know who the Code Toad is."

Tim listened to them. It felt good to hear what they said. Tim couldn't wait to see if someone would find out what the message said.

Again, Scott was the only one who could read the message and he just had to find out who made the code. All of a sudden, he had a plan of his own.

When Scott got home after school he called Jason. "I think I know how to trap the Code Toad," he said.

The next day there was another message on every chair. This time, to Tim's surprise, there was even one for him. It looked like this—

Tim read it one way. It didn't mean anything to him. Then he read it another way. It didn't make sense at all. At last he thought of how it went. He only read a word with one black cat after it. Now it read—

REPORT TO THE GYM AFTER SCHOOL

At last school was over. All day Tim had waited to find out who or what would be in front of the gym. To his surprise it was Scott.

"Are you the Black Cat?" he asked.

"If you are the Code Toad," said Scott. "You were the only one who could read my message," Scott told him. "So it could only be you." He laughed. "I thought it was you all along."

Tim laughed, too. "That was a good trick."

"Why don't we try it again?" said Scott. "We can work out another code right now."

"Good!" said Tim. "We can do it at my house. I have a code book."

They had to run for their bus. Now Tim's heavy bag felt light.

Thinking and Writing About the Selection

1. What was Tim's one wish?

2. What did Tim's first secret message say?

3. Do you think it was hard for Tim not to tell that he was the Code Toad? Why?

4. Why did Tim's heavy bag feel light after he met the Black Cat?

Applying the Key Skill
Inflectional Endings

Number your paper from 1 to 3. Read the sentences below and look at the words underneath each sentence. Then write the word that would complete each sentence on your paper.

1. Jason is the ___ soccer player on the team.
   a. faster   b. fastest

2. Tim is the ___ boy in school.
   a. newer   b. newest

3. This code is ___ than the last one.
   a. harder   b. hardest

SKILLS activity

SEQUENCE OF EVENTS

Most stories have a plan. In the plan the things that take place in the story are told in some kind of order. Words like **first**, **next**, and **last** show the order. Words like **second**, **third**, and **after** can show order, too. When you read look for these words and think about the order.

ACTIVITY A   Read this story about Tim. Think about the plan of the story. Then write the answer to each question on your paper. Use complete sentences.

Tim hated his first day in school. First he watched the boys and girls play soccer, but he didn't play. Then, on the way home, he didn't have a friend to sit with him. When he got home, he thought of something he could do to make some friends.

1. What did Tim do first at school?
2. What did Tim do last in the story?
3. What words helped you know the order of the plan?

ACTIVITY B Read the story and think about its plan.
Then read the sentences below the story.

Jane wanted to have an aquarium. The first
thing she did was to get an aquarium, plants,
and some fish. After she got home, she put
water in the aquarium. Next, she put in the plants
and her fish. Then Jane gave the fish some food.
Jane was happy with her new aquarium.

Jane put fish in the aquarium.
Jane got an aquarium.
Jane put in the water.
Jane gave food to the fish.

1. Write the sentence that tells what Jane did first.
2. Then write the sentence that tells what
   Jane did last.
3. Write the words in the story
   that show you the order
   Jane did things.

I DON'T LIKE READING

Virginia Arnold

Bets loved to skate and play soccer. But she didn't like to read . . . until she met Owl and Caterpillar. They have a message for Bets.

"It's time to read, Bets," said Mother.

"But I haven't tried my brand new skates yet," said Bets. She skated to the street.

"Betty Anne, come here now!" cried Mother.

When Mother spoke like that, it was a sign to move—and move quickly. Bets skated back to the porch.

"After you read for a while, you can try your new skates," Mother said.

"Do I have to read the whole book?" asked Bets.

"Oh, Bets!" said Mother. "You may like this book. You picked it out at the library. I'll read with you," she said.

Just as they sat down on the porch steps, Bets's brother came out to say there was a call for Mother.

"Bets, read your book until I get back," said Mother. "Then I'll read with you." Mother ran into the house.

The porch was so hot. Bets's eyes felt heavy. She made a face at the book. She loved to skate and swim. She loved to play soccer, but she hated to read. Her mother was a librarian and loved to read. And so did her father. Her brother loved to read so much that he worked at the library after school.

"Why am I the only one in the family who doesn't like to read?" she thought.

"How would I know?" whispered a little voice. "Have you tried to like reading?"

"She could be tired," said a gruff voice. "She looks bad to me, but then anything that doesn't have feathers looks bad to me."

Bets opened her eyes wide. "Who said that?" she asked.

"Who said what?" said the little voice. "There are two of us you know."

"I spoke second," said the gruff voice. "Caterpillar spoke first. You spoke third."

"Who are you?" asked Bets. "Where are you?"

"We are right here. Open the book a little," said a little voice.

Bets opened the book. There was a
picture of a caterpillar and an owl. As she
looked, the owl suddenly said, "Come in!
Come in! It's hot when you hold the book
open like that!"

Bets never did know how she did it,
but there she was, on a chair, in a little
house with an owl and a caterpillar looking
at her.

"This whole thing is silly," cried Bets.
"How did I get here?"

"I asked you in," said the owl. "And in you came," said Caterpillar. "Now back to what we were saying. Have you tried to like reading? Why don't you like reading?"

"I don't know," said Bets.

"You must know," said Owl. "You are the one who doesn't like it. Now as for me, I love to read."

"I can take it or leave it," Caterpillar said. "Do you know how to read?"

"Yes," said Bets, "I just don't like it. I just don't see why I need to read. I watch TV and learn things."

Owl said, "When you watch TV, people tell you what to learn. When you read, you can pick anything you want to learn. You can find a book about anything you want to know."

"I never thought of it that way," said Bets.

Caterpillar cried, "Owl, I think we can help her with a 'show her what reading is for' trip!"

"Oh, no," said Owl. "First, I am tired. Second, I might miss lunch . . ."

"And third," said Caterpillar, "you know you love it. Come on."

"What is going on?" asked Bets.

"Just get on my back and be quiet," said Owl. "I must be back in time for lunch and my nap or I get very cross. If people had feathers, I would not mind so much!"

"Hold on! One, two, three! Away we go!" shouted Caterpillar.

In a second, they flew out toward a sign by the sea.

"Can you read that?" asked Caterpillar.

"Do not swim! Sharks!" read Bets.

"If you couldn't read and went for a swim there, you would be a shark dinner," said Caterpillar.

"I never thought of that," said Bets.

They flew over a desert. "See that man reading a map? If he couldn't read, he might never find water," said Owl. Then, they flew down to a library.

"Books can help you do the things you like to do better," said Caterpillar. "Here are three books. These two could help you play soccer better. This third one is about a girl who likes to skate."

"Let me look," cried Bets.

"Not now," said Owl. "We have a good deal more to see and I feel lunch coming on."

They flew on and went to hear a storyteller tell a story. Just as the tiger was going to eat the boy, Owl said, "Come on. We must go."

"But I want to hear the whole story," cried Bets.

"It is in the library, but you never read it," said Caterpillar.

In a second, they were back at the little house. Owl said, "It's time for you to go. We don't have lunch for three."

Bets said, "Don't you want to know if I like reading now?"

Caterpillar said, "Only you can make up your mind about that."

Bets said, "I never thought reading made so much sense. I never thought about why people needed to read."

"If you had feathers, you might think more," said Owl as he walked out of the room.

"Don't mind him," said Caterpillar.

"Good luck," Owl called as he flew away.

Tap, tap, tap. Three drops of water fell on Bets. "Wait," she called to her friends. "Do you know water is coming in your roof? Wait! Wait!"

"Bets, Bets, Bets! Wake up and come in out of the rain," called Mother for the third time. "You will get soaking wet."

Bets opened her eyes. Here she was on her own porch at her own house. She looked quickly at her book, but the owl and caterpillar didn't move.

She ran up the steps into the house.

"Mother," she called. "Do I have a story for you! And it's about reading!"

Thinking and Writing About the Selection

1. Where did Bets get the book that her mother wanted her to read?

2. What things did Bets like to do?

3. Why did Owl think it was better to read than to watch TV?

4. Why do you think Bets liked the 'show her what reading is for' trip?

Applying the Key Skill
Realism and Fantasy

Write these headings on your paper.

    Real   Make-Believe

Write each sentence under the right heading.

1. Bets and her mother read a book on the porch steps.

2. Bets sits in a small house and talks with an owl and a caterpillar.

3. Mother calls Bets to come into the house and eat lunch.

4. Bets gets on Owl's back and they fly toward the sea.

Reading

A story is a special thing.
    The ones that I have read,
They do not stay inside the books.
    They stay inside my head.

Marchette Chute

AT THE LIBRARY

Marlyn Mangus

*Bets began to use the library after
she met Owl and Caterpillar.
You, too, may want to use the
library to find something
to read, or something to do.*

Books, books, and more books! That may be how you think of a library. The word *library* comes from a very old word for "book." A library is a collection of books.

A library may be little or big. You and your family may have a little library at home. A home library has books you like. It may have books you use to find information, too.

A school library is big. It has books to
help you with your school work. Your
school library may be called a media center.
A media center has other things, as well as
books. It may have records, a picture to
look at, or a game to play.

A public library is for all of us. It is a very big collection of books of all kinds. People of every age can use it. Some people go to the library for books of stories they want to read. Other people may go there to look up information. Still other people go to the library to read through magazines and newspapers. No one has to pay money to use the library.

A library may have a huge number of books. Where is each one put? In a library, one kind of book is put with other books of the same kind. Story books are all put in one place. Information books are put in other places. The librarian can show you where to find each kind of book.

A book may have information about owls, elephants, plants, or computers. Some books have information about all kinds of things. You can find information quickly in these books. This picture shows some of these information books. Can you name them?

Did you know that you can take some library books home? To do this, you have to have a library card. Your library may let you have a card when you can sign your own name.

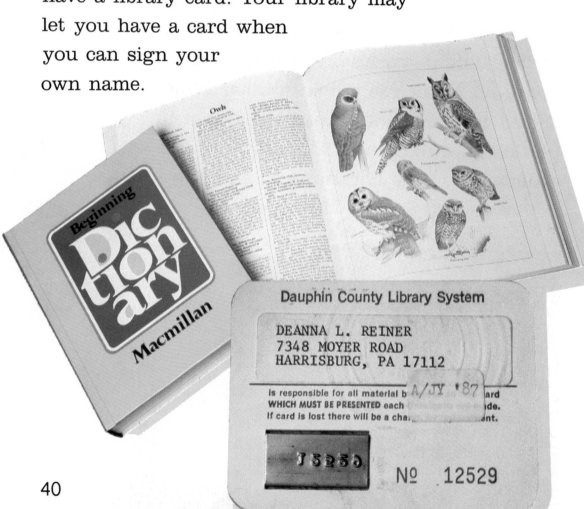

Take your library card and the book you want to the librarian. A date will be put on a card inside the book. You have to bring the book back on or before that date. If you forget and don't bring it back, there will be a fine. A fine is money you have to pay if you keep a book too long.

A public library may have more than story and information books. Newspapers and magazines help people keep up with what is going on. A library may have books in Braille for people who are blind. It may have computers you can use to find information. It has things for people of every age.

QUIET
PLEASE

There is more to do at a library than just read. There may be a storyteller or someone to read stories to boys and girls one day. You may watch a show on another day. There may be people who will tell you how to make things or do things.

One last word: when you go through a library, you may see signs that say, "QUIET, PLEASE." A library is a place for whispers. When you whisper, you don't bother the other people who have come there to read and work.

A library is a place where you can learn and have fun, too. There are books to read and things to do. It is a good place to know about.

Thinking and Writing About the Selection

1. Why do people use the library?

2. Who will help you find things in the library?

3. Tell why the sign in the library says, "QUIET, PLEASE."

 4. What would you like to do at the library?

Applying the Key Skill
Recall Details

Think about the story you have just read. Then complete the sentences with the correct answer on your paper.

1. A library is ___.
   a. a game to play
   b. a collection of books

2. Along with books, some libraries also have ___.
   a. records and games to play
   b. a place to skate

3. If you have a library card, you can ___.
   a. get a librarian to help you
   b. take a book home with you

RECALL DETAILS

The stories we read all have a main idea. But stories also have many facts that tell about the people, animals, places, and things that happen in the story. As you read, think about the facts and try to remember them.

ACTIVITY A Read the paragraph below. Then complete each sentence. Write the sentences on your paper.

Bets was late for her soccer game at the park. She put on her skates. She put her soccer ball in a bag. She skated to the park. Bets got there just in time for the game.

1. Bets had to get _____.
   home
   to a soccer game
   to school

2. She put on her _____.
   shoes
   skates
   socks

3. The soccer game was _____.

       at school

       at the library

       at the park

4. She put _____ in her bag.

       a soccer ball

       her skates

       a book

ACTIVITY B Read the paragraph about owls. Then write the answers to the questions on your paper. Use complete sentences.

Have you ever seen an owl? Owls live in the woods. They have big eyes, feathers and a little tail. Owls sleep in the day. At night they look for food. An owl might find a mouse, a frog, or a bug to eat. When an owl is flying, it can't be heard.

1. Where do owls live?
2. What do owls look like?
3. When do owls sleep?
4. What do owls do at night?
5. What do owls eat?

The Name Day

Gibbs Davis

Maria

Sonja
Adrienne

Name

Alexandra

You can find a book of names at the library.
What does your name mean? Would you
change your name for a day if you could?
Read and find out what Mei-Lan and Mary
think of their names.

Mary never liked her name. In every school it was the same thing. There were too many Marys. Her mother and father shouldn't have called her Mary in the first place. Thanks to them, she was just another name.

All afternoon Mary had sat alone in the library trying to think of a new name.

She wished she lived someplace like Mexico. Then, her name would be MARIA. Smiling, Mary picked up one of her best pencils and wrote MARIA. It looked good on paper, much better than just Mary.

Mary watched the new girl in school walk into the library alone.

"Hi, Mei-Lan," said Ms. Bloom, the school librarian. Mei-Lan asked Ms. Bloom for a book.

When Mei-Lan got the book she wanted, she carried it over to where Mary was and sat down. After looking through it, she began to write very quickly.

Mei-Lan, what a pretty name, thought Mary. Some people have all the luck. Before Mary could say anything, the girl had walked out the door. On her way out, Mei-Lan had dropped her book.

When Mary picked up the book on the floor, her eyes opened wide with surprise. It was a book of names!

Mary carried her things outside to wait for the school bus home. When she saw Mei-Lan by the bus stop she walked over to meet her.

"Hi, my name is Mary."

The girl looked up. "I would do anything to have a name like Mary," said Mei-Lan. "I was trying to find a new name in the library this afternoon."

"I know," said Mary. She gave Mei-Lan back her book of names. "This fell on the floor."

"Thanks," whispered Mei-Lan.

"Mei-Lan is so pretty," said Mary, smiling. "I think it's the best girl's name in our whole school."

"You do?" said Mei-Lan.

Just then the bus came up the street.

The girls ran to meet the bus. "Please sit next to me," said Mary.

Mei-Lan sat down next to Mary. She had just made her first friend.

The next afternoon, Mary and Mei-Lan
saw a big paper sign outside the library.
It read:

NAME DAY
Come to the school library this afternoon
for a report about Name Day.

"Name Day. What is that?" asked
Mei-Lan.

"Well, there is one way to find out," said
Mary, as she opened the library door.

Inside, Ms. Bloom spoke to a room full
of people.

"How many of us at one time have
wished for a brand new first name? Hold up
your hand if you have."

One hand after another went up.

"I didn't know so many people felt as we
do," whispered Mei-Lan.

Ms. Bloom went on. "I thought we could try something new. On Name Day you can each pick out a new name, and the whole school will call you by that name for a full day.

"Try to pick a name that will mean something to you. Look at your family tree. Ask your mother and father why they gave you your name. Think about it."

The next afternoon Mary carried her pencils and paper outside. She was going to meet Mei-Lan at the playground. Thanks to Mei-Lan and her book, they were going to have the best names in school.

Just then Mary saw Mei-Lan. She was walking so quickly that the tops of her feet spun on the ice. "We have to get to work," said Mei-Lan. She sat down and opened the name book. As she read the names out loud, Mary wrote them all down on paper. There were first and last names, boys and girls names, and even family names.

When it was time to go back inside, Mary's head spun with names. "I never thought I would say this, but I am tired of names."

"I know what you mean," said Mei-Lan.

On Name Day, Mary walked through school. She wanted to show off her name tag. It read: ALEXANDRA.

She wanted to show her new name to Mei-Lan. She rushed into the library to find her.

"You have to hear this," whispered Mary.

"Don't you want to know my new name first?" asked Mei-Lan.

"Yes," said Mary.

"You won't tease me?" asked Mei-Lan.

"No," said Mary.

Mei-Lan showed her name tag. It read MARY!

Suddenly Mary felt glad.

Name Day was so much fun Mary and Mei-Lan hated to leave school. They were the last people to get on the bus home.

"Did you look up your name in the library?" asked Mary.

"Yes," said Mei-Lan and showed Mary another book of names. "It says Mei-Lan is the same as Pretty Flower."

Mary thought of all the other Marys on her street. "I wish my name could mean something, too." She looked sad.

"It does mean something," said Mei-Lan. "It means something to me."

"What?" asked Mary.

"Best friend," said Mei-Lan smiling, and she put away her book of names.

Thinking and Writing About the Selection

1. Why didn't Mary like her name?

2. What did Ms. Bloom tell the children they would do on Name Day?

3. Why do you think Mary picked the name Alexandra for Name Day?

4. Do you think that Mary likes her name better now than she did before?

Applying the Key Skill
Initial Consonant Clusters

Use the letters below to finish the words.
Write the sentences on your paper.

    sm   sp   sk   sc

1. One day Mary looked out the door, and the ___y was blue!

2. Winter was over and Mary didn't need to wear her ___arf and hat. She stopped to ___ell a flower on her way to Mei-Lan's house.

3. Soon Mary and Mei-Lan would ___in on their skates!

My Other Name

Jennifer's my other name
    (It's make-believe
    and just a game.)

I'm really Anne,
But just the same
I'd much
    much
    rather
    have a name
    like Jennifer.

(So, if you can
    don't call me Anne.)

Myra Cohn Livingston

Rumpelstiltskin

Retold by Margaret H. Lippert

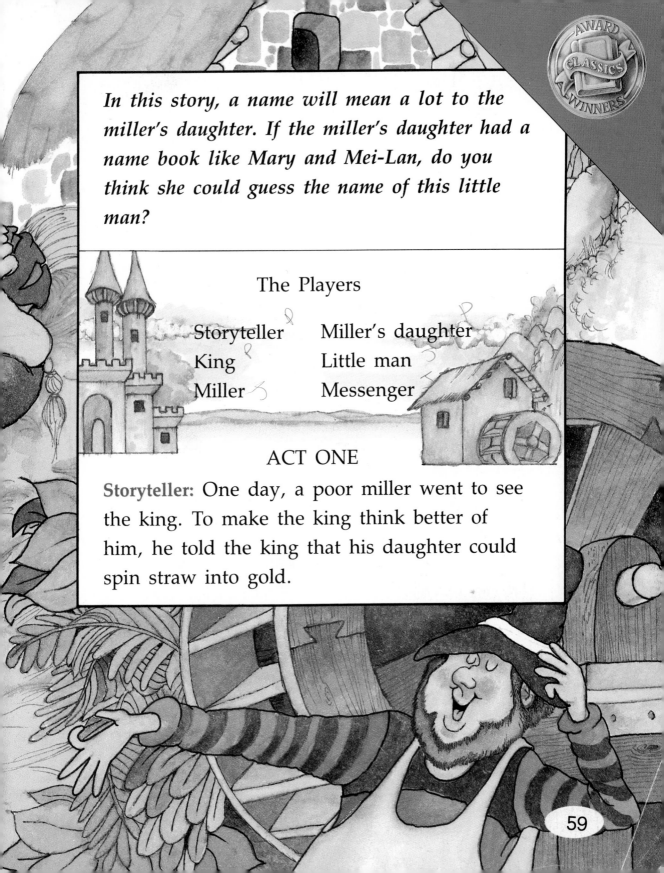

In this story, a name will mean a lot to the miller's daughter. If the miller's daughter had a name book like Mary and Mei-Lan, do you think she could guess the name of this little man?

The Players

Storyteller	Miller's daughter
King	Little man
Miller	Messenger

ACT ONE

Storyteller: One day, a poor miller went to see the king. To make the king think better of him, he told the king that his daughter could spin straw into gold.

King: I do not know anyone who can spin straw into gold. I would like to meet your daughter. Tell her to come and see me.

Miller: I will tell her the king wishes to see her. She will be here in the morning.

Storyteller: That night, the miller told his daughter what the king had said. The next morning, she went to the king's castle.

King (sternly): Your father said that you can spin straw into gold. Now I will see if what he said is true. Here is a room full of straw, and a spinning wheel. Spin all this straw into gold, or in the morning you will die.

Storyteller: The king went away. The girl was alone in the room full of straw. She did not know how to spin straw into gold. Because she was scared of what would happen to her, she began to cry. Just then, a little man came in.

Little man: What is the matter?

Miller's daughter: I have to spin this straw into gold. I do not know how to do it, and I am scared of what will happen to me.

Little man: What will you give me if I spin it for you?

Miller's daughter: I will give you my necklace.

Storyteller: The girl gave the little man her necklace. Then the little man sat down at the spinning wheel and began to spin the straw into gold. When he had spun all of the straw into gold, he went away. In the morning, the king came back.

King (as he takes some of the gold in his hands): GOLD! This is gold. So what your father said was true. I did not know anyone could spin straw into gold.

Storyteller: The king led the miller's daughter to another room.

King: Here is another room, with more straw than the first. I want you to spin all this straw into gold, too. If you do not spin it all into gold by morning, you will die.

Storyteller: Again the girl was alone. Again she began to cry, and again the little man came in.

Little man: Now what is the matter?

Miller's daughter: I have to spin all this straw into gold, too.

Little man: What will you give me if I spin it for you?

Miller's daughter: I will give you my ring.

Storyteller: The girl gave the little man her ring, and he began to spin. Before long, he had spun all of the straw into gold. Then he went away. In the morning, the king came back.

King: This time you did even better! I have one more room full of straw. If you spin that straw into gold, I will make you my queen.

Storyteller: After the king went away, the girl began to cry. For the third time, the little man came in.

Little man: What will you give me if I spin the straw for you this time?

Miller's daughter: I have nothing more to give.

Little man: Then give me the first child you have after you are queen.

Storyteller: The poor girl did not know what to do, but at last she told the little man he could have her first child. By morning, he had spun all the straw into gold. Then he went away, and the king came in.

King: You did it again! Now you will be my queen.

Storyteller: So that very morning, the king made the miller's daughter his queen.

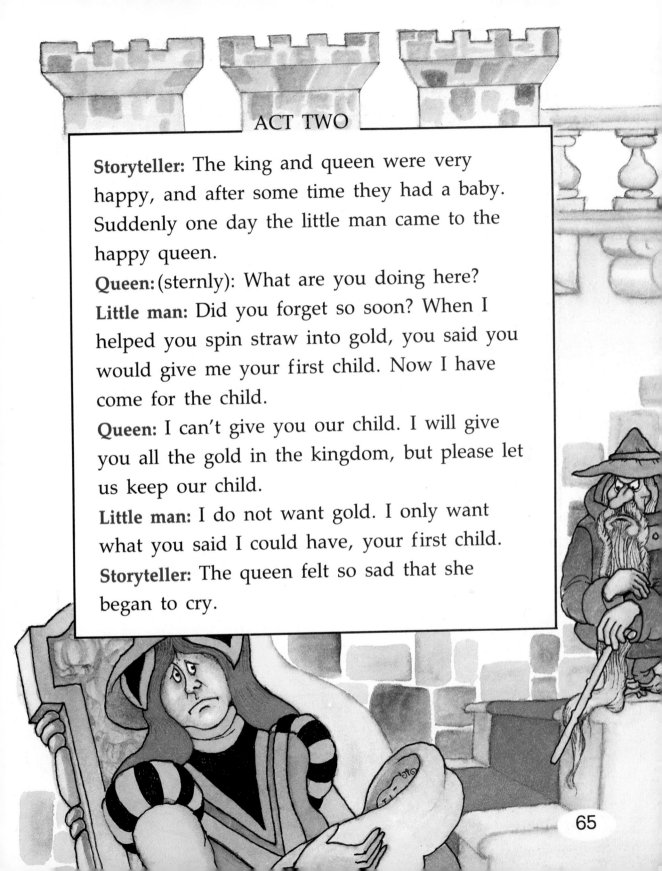

Storyteller: The king and queen were very happy, and after some time they had a baby. Suddenly one day the little man came to the happy queen.

Queen: (sternly): What are you doing here?

Little man: Did you forget so soon? When I helped you spin straw into gold, you said you would give me your first child. Now I have come for the child.

Queen: I can't give you our child. I will give you all the gold in the kingdom, but please let us keep our child.

Little man: I do not want gold. I only want what you said I could have, your first child.

Storyteller: The queen felt so sad that she began to cry.

Little man: I do not like to see you so sad. If you can guess my name, I will let you keep your baby. But if after three days you can't guess my name, you will have to give your baby to me.

Storyteller: The queen was up all night thinking of names. In the morning, the little man came.

Little man: Can you guess my name?

Queen: Is it Tom?

Little man: No!

Queen: Is it Harry?

Little man: No!

Storyteller: The queen went on and on but she could not guess his name. The same day, the queen asked all her friends to tell her all the names they had heard. The second morning the little man came again, but still she could not guess his name. Then the queen asked a messenger to come to her.

Queen: I need new names. I have one more morning to guess the name of the little man. Go as quickly as you can, and ask all the people you see to tell you all the names they know.

Storyteller: The messenger came back late that night, and told the queen all the names that the people had told him.

Queen: Is that all?

Messenger: That is all the names people told me, but I did hear one more name. As the sun went down in the woods, I saw a little house made of mud and sticks by the path. In front of the house there was a little man. He was laughing and I heard him say:

> Soon I'll bring the queen's child here
> She will never win my game
> For no one in the kingdom knows
> That Rumpelstiltskin is my name.

Storyteller: In the morning the little man came for the last time.

Little man: Can you guess my name?

Queen: Is it Ebenezer?

Little man: No!

Queen: Is it Spindleshank?

Little man: No!

Queen: Is it . . . Rumpelstiltskin?

Little man: Who told you that? Who told you that?

Storyteller: The little man was so mad that he jumped into the ground until not even his head could be seen, and no one saw him again.

Thinking and Writing About the Selection

1. What did the miller tell the king?

2. What two things did the miller's daughter give the little man?

3. Do you think the miller should have told the king that his daughter could spin straw into gold? Why?

 4. Do you think Rumpelstiltskin was a good helper? Why?

Applying the Key Skill
Context Clues

Find the meaning of the underlined word.
Write the word and its meaning on your paper.

1. Rumpelstiltskin <u>raced</u> by the miller's daughter to get to the spinning wheel.
   a. ran   b. blew   c. banged

2. The King and Queen ate their <u>meal</u> at the miller's house last night.
   a. chairs   b. dinner   c. turtle

3. The little girl began to <u>pull</u> on her mother's hand.
   a. open   b. trick   c. tug

Margaret H. Lippert

There are three kinds of stories I like to tell: true stories about funny or interesting things that happen to people in my family, folk tales, and stories I make up, that no one has ever heard, or thought of before.

I love to tell stories and to write them down. When I am asked to write a story I feel scared because I don't know how to begin, and I feel excited because I know I will live that story for a while.

As a writer, I don't know who my words will reach. That is why I find being an author so thrilling. I don't know you, but now you know a little about me, just by reading these words. I like that.

TIME FOR A RHYME

Read what the messenger hears the little man say in the folk tale "Rumpelstiltskin."

> Soon I'll bring the queen's child here
> She will never win my <u>game</u>
> For no one in the kingdom knows
> That Rumpelstiltskin is my <u>name</u>.

Look at the words with a line under them. Say the words, *game* and *name.* These words sound alike. They have the same vowel and ending sound.

Read the sentence parts below. Match the parts so the last words rhyme and make a sentence.

1. A day in the sun   if you are hot.
2. This is the spot   can be so much fun.

Can you think of some words to rhyme with these words? Can you write sentences with parts that rhyme?

> spun   best   ring   code

Gloria Who Might Be My Best Friend

Anne Cameron

Julian does not try to guess the new girl's
name. He finds out that one way to find out
the name of someone new is just to ask,
"Who are you?" That someone new may be
a friend.

If you have a girl for a friend, people find out and laugh at you. That's why I didn't want a girl for a friend—not until I met Gloria.

One day I saw a van a block from my house. A man was bringing in chairs and tables and books and boxes. I watched for a while, and suddenly I heard a voice.

"Who are you?"

I looked and there was a girl in red. She looked the same age as me. She had two braids.

"I am Julian," I said. "Who are you?"

"I am Gloria," she said. "I come from Newport. Can you do a cartwheel?"

She spun sideways and did two cartwheels on the grass.

I never did a cartwheel before. I wanted to
do one like Gloria's. My hands went down in the
grass, my feet went up and I fell over.

I looked at Gloria to see if she was laughing
at me. If she was laughing at me, I was going to
go home and forget about her.

But she just looked at me and said, "You have
to keep trying again and again," and then I liked her.

"I know where there is a bird's nest in your
yard," I said.

"Where?" Gloria asked.

I showed her where a robin lives. Gloria
jumped up on the tree and looked in.

"Would you like to come over to my house?"
I asked.

"All right," Gloria said, "if it is all right with
my mother."

It was all right, so Gloria and I went to my
house, and I showed her my games and my rock
collection.

"I wish you would live here a long time," I
told Gloria.

"I wish I would, too." Gloria said, "I know the
best way to make wishes,"

"What is that?" I asked.

"First you make a kite. Do you know how to
make one?"

"Yes," I said. "I know how to make good
kites because my father showed me. We make
them out of two crossed sticks and some
newspapers."

We went out into the yard and made a kite. I
tied on the kite string and got rags for the tail.

"Do you have some paper and two pencils?" Gloria asked. "Because now we make the wishes."

I didn't know what she was going to do, but I went in the house and got pencils and paper.

"All right," Gloria said. "Every wish you want to have come true you write down on paper. You don't tell me your wishes, and I don't tell you mine. If you tell, your wishes don't come true."

Gloria sat down on the ground again and began to write her wishes. I wanted to see what they were—but I went to another place in the yard and wrote my own wishes. I wrote:

1. I wish I could play soccer better than anyone.
2. I wish I could ride in a plane.
3. I wish Gloria would stay here and be my best friend.

I went over to Gloria with my wishes in my hand.

"How many wishes did you make?" Gloria asked.

"Three," I said. "How many did you make?"

"Two," Gloria said.

I wanted to know what they were.

"Now we put the wishes on the tail of the kite," Gloria said. "Every time we tie a rag on the tail, we place a wish in it."

I tied mine in, and then Gloria tied in hers, and we carried the kite into the yard.

"You hold the tail," Gloria said, "and I will tug."

We ran to the open yard by the house.

The kite began to move up into the sky. Soon the kite was flying over the roof of my house and was floating toward the sun.

"When we take the kite down," Gloria said, "there shouldn't be one wish in the tail. When the wind takes all your wishes, that's when you know it's going to work."

The kite stayed up for a long time. The kite looked like a little black dot in the sun.

"Can we take it in?" I asked.

"All right," Gloria said.

The kite came down and down until it fell at our feet.

We looked at the tail. The wishes were not there.

Could it be that I would get to be good at soccer and have a ride in a plane? And Gloria would be my best friend?

"Gloria," I said, "did you wish we would be friends?"

"You should not ask me that!" Gloria laughed.

"I know," I said. But inside I was smiling. I guessed one thing Gloria wished for, that we would be best friends.

Thinking and Writing About the Selection

1. What would Julian do if Gloria laughed at him?

2. How did Julian make a kite?

3. What three things did Julian know about?

 4. What three wishes would you put in the tail of a kite?

Applying the Key Skill
Summarize

Read the sentences. Which sentence below has the same meaning? Write that sentence on your paper.

Julian wished that he could play soccer better than anyone. He also wished that he could fly in a plane.

a. Julian wished that he could play better soccer and go up in an airplane.

b. Julian wished that he could fly in a plane so that he would be better than anyone.

c. Julian wished that he could be better than anyone so he could play soccer and fly in an airplane.

I'm Up Here

I'm up here.
You're down there.
And nothing in that space between us
But a mile of air.
Where I sail:
Clouds pass.
Where you run:
Green grass.
Where I float:
Birds sing.
One thin thing there is
That holds us close together:
Kite string.

Karla Kuskin

A Kite of Your Own

Loretta Kaim

Gloria and Julian could tie a message to the tail of their kite. With these directions and a good wind, you will have a kite of your own. A friend may want to help just as Gloria helped Julian.

Have you watched a kite as it flew overhead? Did you wish that you had one, too? Well, you can have a kite of your own!

The price of a kite may be as little as $2.00. But you won't have to spend anything at all if you make your own kite. You can find most of the things you need to make a kite right in your home.

There are many kinds of kites. There are flat kites, box kites, and dragon kites. The following directions tell you how to make a flat kite. If you follow them step by step, you will have a kite.

First you will need two long sticks. One stick should be 30 inches long. The other stick should be 24 inches long. Your sticks should be about as wide as pencils.

Ask someone to help you make a little cut at each end of the sticks, as the picture shows.

Now take your long stick and draw a dot 8 inches from one end. Draw a dot 12 inches from one end of the other stick. Then put the sticks across each other to make a t. The sticks should cross at the dot. Wind a string around the place where the sticks cross and tie it. To make this tie even stronger, it should be covered with a coat of glue.

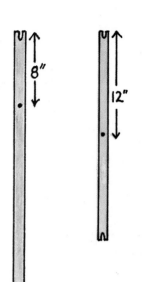

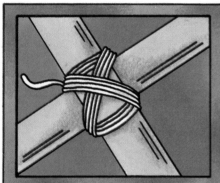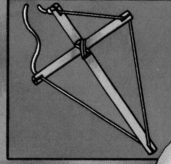

When the glue is dry, put a string into the top cut. Then run the string through the cut at the end of each stick. Place the string into each cut as you go along. Tie the string back at the top.

Now take some more string and wind it again around the end of each stick. This will help hold the first string in place. It will help keep your sticks from cracking, too.

Now it's time for your kite to be covered. Sometimes people use cloth, but most kites are covered with paper. If you use newspaper or a big bag, you won't have to spend anything for paper.

Put your paper on the floor and place the sticks on top of it. Hold the sticks in place with one hand. Trace around the string with the other. Then take the sticks off the paper. Do not cut on the trace, but cut 2 inches to the right of where you made the trace. Look at this picture before you cut. You will need to cut off each end of the paper, as the picture shows.

Now you can draw a picture on your kite. Draw a face, an animal, or anything at all. Make your picture big, so you can see it when your kite is flying overhead.

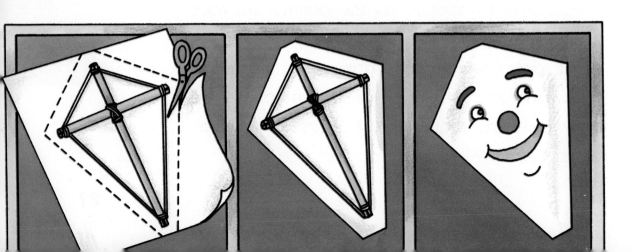

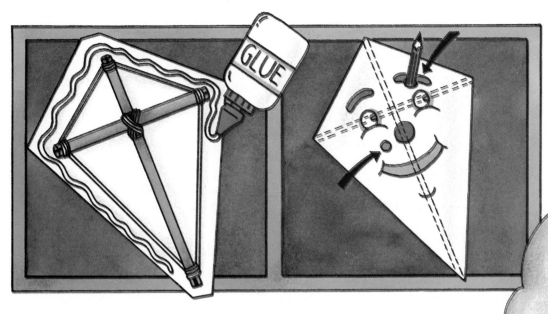

Now put your paper back on the floor
with the picture down. Put the sticks on top of
it. The stick that runs across should be on the
top. Put a lot of glue on the outside 2 inches
of the paper of your kite. Then push the
paper onto the string. Push down hard to
help the paper stay in place.

Wait for the glue to dry. Then make one
dot to the right of where the sticks cross and
another dot under it, as the picture shows.
Push something little through the paper at
each dot. (Pencils do a good job.) To make
your kite stronger, glue a cloth or paper ring
around each dot, on the front and the back
of the kite.

Next you need a ball of string to fly your kite. Hold the kite so you can see your picture. Run the string through one ring, around the crossed sticks, and back out through the other ring. Then tie the string about 3 inches from the kite face.

Last of all, you need a tail. The job of the tail is to keep the kite from going sideways. If your kite does not have a tail it will spin all over the sky and quickly fall to the ground.

You can make a good tail from bits of cloth about 2 inches wide and 6 inches long. Tie these bits to a 13-foot long string. They should be tied on the string every 6 inches or so. After you have tied on as many bits of cloth as you need, tie the string onto your kite. Now your kite has a tail.

Now that you have learned how to make a kite, you will need to make it fly somehow. Have you watched as anyone flew a kite? If not, here are some steps you can follow. As you will soon see, it's not hard at all.

First, find a place where there are not many trees. Trees can block the wind and get in your way.

Put your back to the wind. Ask a helper to take your kite about 25 feet away from you.

When a good wind comes along, tell your helper to toss the kite up. At the same time, you should walk back into the wind. As the wind takes the kite up, let out more string as quickly as you can. If you can get your kite to stay up in the sky, you will know that you have learned all about making a kite!

Thinking and Writing About the Selection

1. Name some things you will need to make a kite.

2. Where do you put the dots at the end of each stick?

3. How can you make your kite stronger?

 4. Write about how it would feel to see the wind take your kite for a ride in the sky.

Applying the Key Skill
Sequence of Events

The sentences below tell how to make a kite. Write the sentences in the correct order.

Then, put the sticks across each other to form a "t."

Next, glue the sticks together.

Last, tie a string and a tail to your kite.

First, you need to get two long sticks.

After that, cover your kite with paper.

WRITING activity

STORY

Prewrite

In "A Kite of Your Own," you read the directions for making a kite. You could make a kite of your own and even tie wishes into its tail as Julian and Gloria did. One of your wishes might be to take a trip. To your surprise, your wish comes true. Before you can say anything, you are as small as a bug and riding on the tail of your own kite. When you get home from your trip, you write a story about it for the newspapers.

Before you write, you need to make a plan for your story. Think about these questions. Your answers will help you plan what you will say in your story.

1. What places did you go to on your trip?
2. Where did you go first?
3. Where did you go next?
4. How or where did your trip end?
5. What can you tell about each place you saw on your trip?

Write

1. Use your plan to write your story.
2. Your first sentence should make people want to read your story. Try this one:

   I will never forget my high-flying ride on the tail of a kite.

3. Write sentences about the places you saw.
4. You may want to use Vocabulary Treasures in your story.
5. Write a title for your story.

Vocabulary Treasures	
floating	creaking
heavy	second

Revise

Read your story. Have a friend read it, too. Think about these things as you revise.

1. Do your sentences tell about the places you saw on your trip?
2. Could someone who reads your story tell one thing about each place? If not, what more can you say to help them?
3. Did you end each sentence with the right punctuation mark?
4. Now write your story again on another paper.

I Wish I Were Back Home

Argentina Palacios

You may feel sad to have to leave a **friend**.
But when you open your first letter **from**
a friend who is away, the message tells **you**
that your friend remembers you.

Delia and Alba were best friends. They lived next
door to each other in Patzcuaro, Mexico. When
Delia's father finds a new job at an aquarium in
New York City, Delia and her family will have to
move there for two years. She is sad to leave her
home and her grandpa and grandma. But, most of
all she is sad to leave Alba.

Dear Alba,   New York, New York

  I wish I were back home. I don't have one
friend here. My father goes to work at the
aquarium and he's away for most of the day.
Mother and I began looking for a house, but no
luck yet. There are so many people in the city.
People are so rushed all the time. They move
very quickly from the time their day begins until
it gets dark. They look angry to me. I think
about the people in our city in Mexico and wish
I were there.

  My mother is looking for a job now. She
reads all the newspapers. She would like to work
as a librarian in the fall when I am in school.

  Tell your grandpa that Delia remembers his
stories. Your best friend remembers you when she
is awake and when she is sleeping.

                    Love,
                    Delia

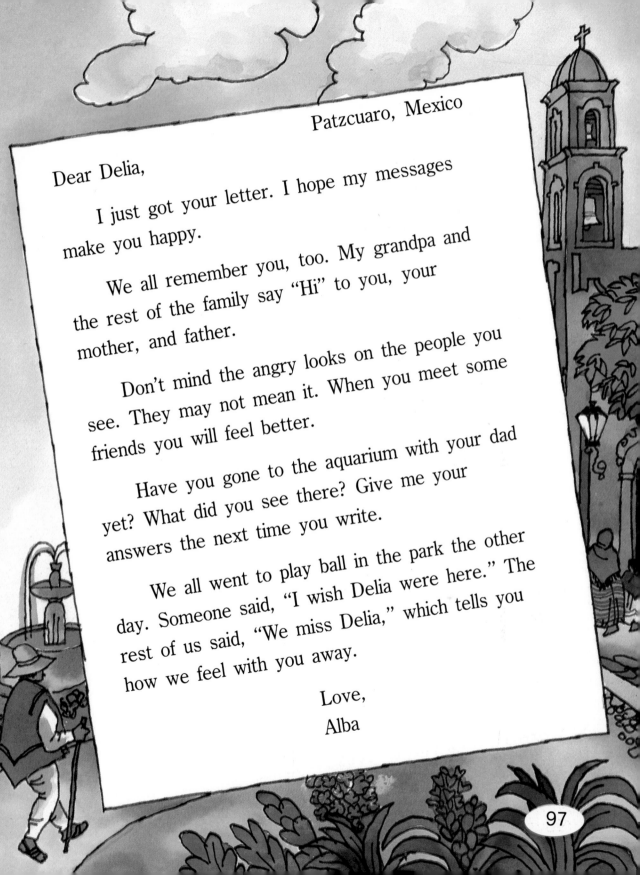

Patzcuaro, Mexico

Dear Delia,

I just got your letter. I hope my messages make you happy.

We all remember you, too. My grandpa and the rest of the family say "Hi" to you, your mother, and father.

Don't mind the angry looks on the people you see. They may not mean it. When you meet some friends you will feel better.

Have you gone to the aquarium with your dad yet? What did you see there? Give me your answers the next time you write.

We all went to play ball in the park the other day. Someone said, "I wish Delia were here." The rest of us said, "We miss Delia," which tells you how we feel with you away.

Love,
Alba

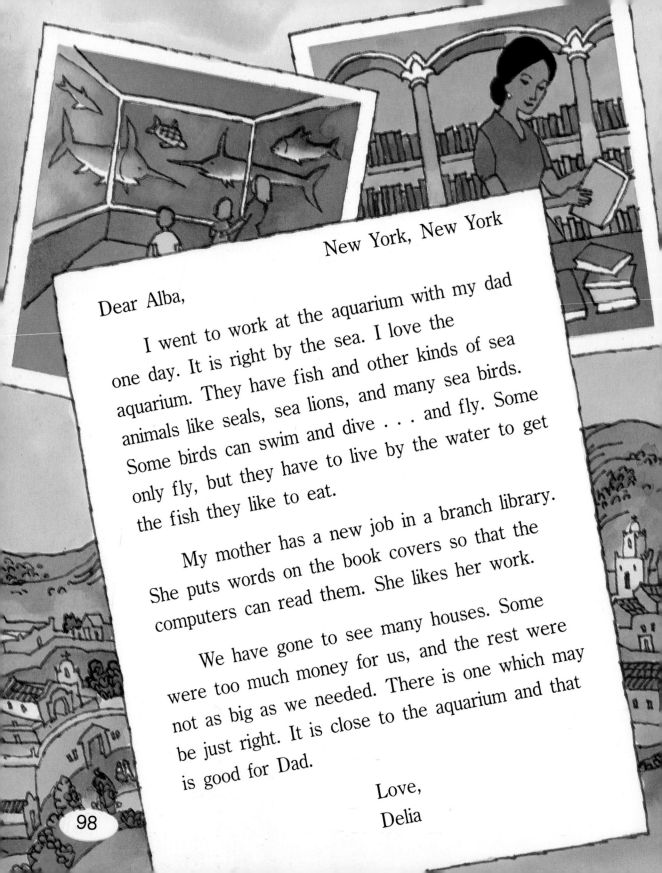

New York, New York

Dear Alba,

I went to work at the aquarium with my dad one day. It is right by the sea. I love the aquarium. They have fish and other kinds of sea animals like seals, sea lions, and many sea birds. Some birds can swim and dive . . . and fly. Some only fly, but they have to live by the water to get the fish they like to eat.

My mother has a new job in a branch library. She puts words on the book covers so that the computers can read them. She likes her work.

We have gone to see many houses. Some were too much money for us, and the rest were not as big as we needed. There is one which may be just right. It is close to the aquarium and that is good for Dad.

Love,
Delia

Dear Delia,   Patzcuaro, Mexico

When you said the aquarium is right by the sea, I thought of our city in Mexico, which is on a lake. Are you by a lake, too?

Do you know what you need before school begins and the days get dark before six o'clock? You need a trip to the zoo. That will make you happy, I know. There has to be a zoo in New York City.

Remember that your friend Alba answers when you write.

Love,
Alba

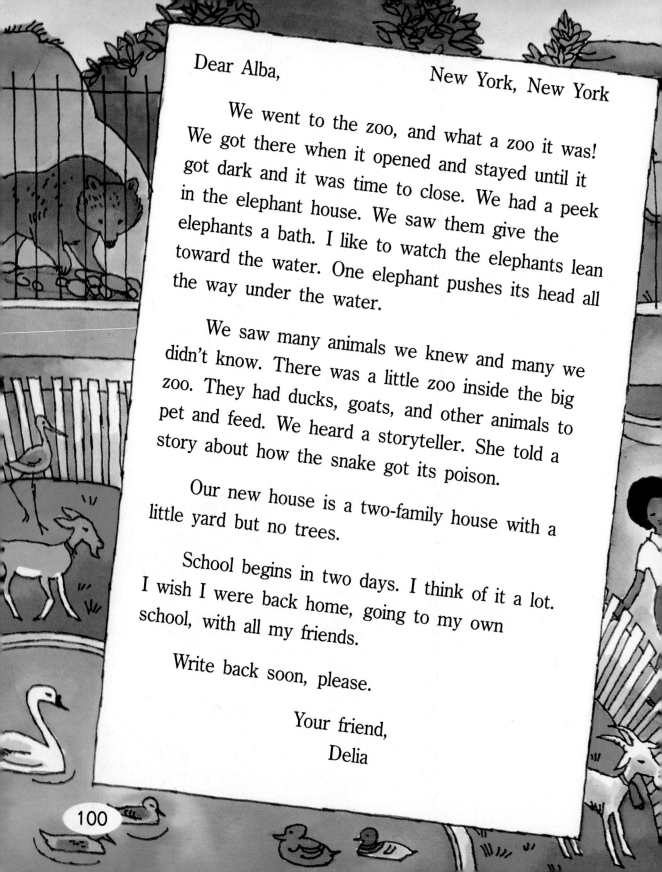

Dear Alba,   New York, New York

We went to the zoo, and what a zoo it was! We got there when it opened and stayed until it got dark and it was time to close. We had a peek in the elephant house. We saw them give the elephants a bath. I like to watch the elephants lean toward the water. One elephant pushes its head all the way under the water.

We saw many animals we knew and many we didn't know. There was a little zoo inside the big zoo. They had ducks, goats, and other animals to pet and feed. We heard a storyteller. She told a story about how the snake got its poison.

Our new house is a two-family house with a little yard but no trees.

School begins in two days. I think of it a lot. I wish I were back home, going to my own school, with all my friends.

Write back soon, please.

Your friend,
Delia

Dear Delia,

Patzcuaro, Mexico

I spoke with your grandma and grandpa after I got your letter. They said they got a letter from you, too. It is so much fun to get a letter from my friend Delia in New York City!

I am happy you went to the zoo. I would like to see that zoo some day, too.

Don't feel so bad. School begins soon and you will make a lot of friends. I hope you don't forget me then. Before you know it, you will be back home.

Love,

Alba

Thinking and Writing About the Selection

1. Why did Delia wish that she were back home?

2. Did Delia like the aquarium? Why?

3. How did this plan to write to each other help Delia and Alba?

4. What do you think Delia's first day at her new school will be like?

Applying the Key Skill
Final Consonant Clusters

Number your paper from 1 to 5. Then use the letters below to finish the words in each sentence. Write the words on your paper.

    ft   sk   st   nk

1. Alba wants to get her friend a gi___.

2. First, she must thi___ of what to get.

3. Alba walks fa___ when she goes to the store.

4. At the store she looks at a so___ toy animal.

5. Then Alba sees a ma___ in the store.

Best Wishes, Ed

James Stevenson

Ed finds that he is all alone on an island of ice. Like Delia in "I Wish I Were Back Home," he begins to miss his friends. Messages help Ed find his way back home to his friends.

Ed lived on a big island of ice with Betty, Freddy, Al, and a lot of other penguins. Every day the penguins had fun as they tossed snowballs and ran across the ice. But they always watched out for Ernest, the big whale. Every time he went by . . . SPLAT! Ed and all the penguins got soaked.

"Watch what you are doing!" Betty would yell. But Ernest swam right by.

"Ernest doesn't even notice penguins," said Ed.

One night when Ed was asleep, he heard a loud noise, like ice cracking. Ed thought it was a dream.

When Ed woke up, he saw that the island of ice was cracking in two. He was all alone on an island of his own.

Ed's friends looked very little as his island floated away. Ed watched until he couldn't see them anymore.

Then he walked all over his island. There was nobody on it at all. At last he came to his own footprints again.

Some birds flew over. Ed waved, but they did not wave back. "I think I will be here the rest of my life," Ed said.

When the day was over, Ed wrote the words "I GIVE UP" in the snow. Then he went to sleep.

The next day a bird woke him up. "Hi," said the bird, "did you write that thing in the snow?"

"Yes," said Ed.

"Could you write something for me?" asked the bird.

"I think so," said Ed. "What do you want?"

"Tell my friends to meet me at the iceberg," said the bird. "Sign it *Talbot*. That is my name."

Talbot flew away, and Ed wrote the message.

MEET ME AT THE ICEBERG.
                        TALBOT

Pretty soon, Talbot's friends flew over and read the message. They waved to Ed, and Ed waved back.

All day long, birds came by and asked Ed to write messages for them. When the day was over, all of the island was covered with messages. Ed was very tired.

Talbot flew down and gave Ed a fish. "You are doing a very good job," said Talbot. "How come you look so sad?"

"I miss my friends on my other island," said Ed.

"Where is your other island?" asked Talbot.

"Way over there someplace," said Ed.

"Too bad you can't fly," said Talbot. "You could see it from the sky."

"Well, I can't fly," said Ed.

"It's not very hard," said Talbot.

"It is for penguins," said Ed. Talbot flew away.

"I think I will spend the rest of my life doing these messages," Ed said.

When Ed got up the next day, he saw a surprise.

ED-THERE'S A MESSAGE FOR YOU
FOLLOW THE SIGNS

He followed the signs until he came to another message.

SIT HERE AND WAIT →

He sat down on the X and waited. Suddenly there was a huge SPLAT! Ed was soaked. It was Ernest, the whale.

"I heard you are looking for a ride to that island with all the penguins on it," said Ernest.

"How did you know?" asked Ed.

"I heard it from Talbot," said Ernest. "Hop on my back."

"Wait one second," said Ed. "I have to leave a message."

Ed quickly wrote the message in the snow.

THANK YOU, TALBOT. BEST WISHES, Ed

Then he got on top of Ernest's back.

Ernest gave three quick splashes with his tail, and then they were flying across the water.

"Ed is back!" yelled Betty.

"At last!" shouted Freddy and Al.

Ed jumped off Ernest's back. "Thanks a lot, Ernest," shouted Ed.

"That's O.K.," said Ernest. "Just don't think you can have a ride every day."

"We are so glad you are back, Ed," said Betty.

"We missed you a lot," said Freddy and Al.

"I missed you," said Ed.

SPLAT! They were all soaked, as Ernest swam away.

"Oh," said Betty, "he did it again!"

"Ernest doesn't notice penguins," said Freddy.

"Sometimes he does," said Ed.

Thinking and Writing About the Selection

1. Who lived on the big island of ice?

2. What did Ed hear when he was asleep?

3. Why was Ed so tired at the end of the day?

4. Do you think that Talbot was a good friend? Why?

Applying the Key Skill
Initial Consonant Clusters

Use the letters below to finish the words in the paragraph. Write the paragraph on your paper.

sw   sn   st

Ed ____ared at all the ____ow coming down. It had snowed for three days. Ed could not see in all that ____ow. He took a ____ep and fell into the water! Just then Ernest ____am by. "This is not a good day to ____im," he said, as he put Ed back on the ice.

REALISM AND FANTASY

Some things that happen in stories are real and some are make-believe. A penguin who writes messages is make-believe. But Delia and Alba were real girls who wrote real messages to each other. When you read, think about what is real and what is make-believe.

ACTIVITY A Look at the pictures. Then read the sentences. On your paper write the sentences that are make-believe.

1. The boy skated across the pond.
2. The bird had two braids.
3. The dragon floated in the sea.
4. The girl kicked the ball to the moon.
5. The kite is in a tree.
6. The whale swam for a long time.

ACTIVITY B Read the story. Write the answers to the questions on your paper. Use complete sentences.

A penguin lived in an aquarium with lots of other penguins and fish. He had food to eat and a spot to sleep. But he wanted to fly. One day he jumped into his plane, waved to his friends, and flew off on a trip to Puerto Rico.

1. Could a penguin live in an aquarium?
2. How is the penguin in this story like a real penguin?
3. Does the penguin in this story do anything that a real penguin would not do?

ALEXANDER CALDER:

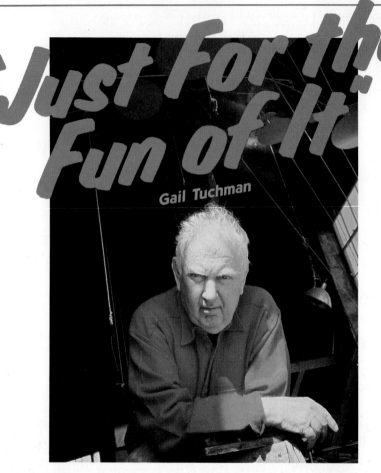

"Just For the Fun of It"

Gail Tuchman

When Alexander Calder was a boy
he liked to look at the circus. He
made animals for people to see. The
circus had a message for Calder. He
put this message into his art.

Alexander Calder tells us many things through his art. In his work, we see his love of life. He liked to watch birds and bugs. He loved to see the red sun each day. He loved to see the moon smiling in the dark of night. Calder loved the circus and animals.

He would notice all the things around him. Each thing, big or little, touched him, and it would find its way into his art. Even now, Calder's art always feels like new— like a surprise.

From the age of eight, Calder began to make little play things. The kinds of play things he made as a child opened the door for the art that followed.

Anyone who knows Calder's work knows that a love of play is what Calder's art is about. Calder could turn a can into a bird, or wood into a chicken. He made bears that could skate and fish that could swim. Calder's work was like a picture that could move.

Chock. (1972). Whitney Museum of American Art.

Circus. (1926). Collection of Nanette Hayes Saxton.

"I want to make things that are fun to look at . . . ," said Calder. "I always loved the circus . . . so I [made] a circus just for the fun of it."

Calder's love for the circus began in the 1920s while he was doing art for magazines. He was asked to go to the Ringling Brothers Barnum and Bailey Circus.

Day after day and night after night, he watched things under the big top. He watched the lions, elephants, and seals do tricks. He watched people spring and turn cartwheels. Suddenly, overhead, someone would step out and walk across the big top as if she were a bird on a string. There was always a surprise.

Kangaroo, a figure from the *Circus.* (1926-31).
Whitney Museum of American Art.

Calder would listen to all the circus sounds. He would listen to the calls of the seals and lions. He would listen to someone singing a song or playing a tune. Calder could tell by listening to the music what was going to happen next.

Then Calder made his own little art circus. He made animals and people from bits of cloth and wood and string. He gave his first circus shows on the floor in his room. Calder would turn on a light to show the circus ring. He put on records so that his friends could listen to "circus" music. Then the circus show began.

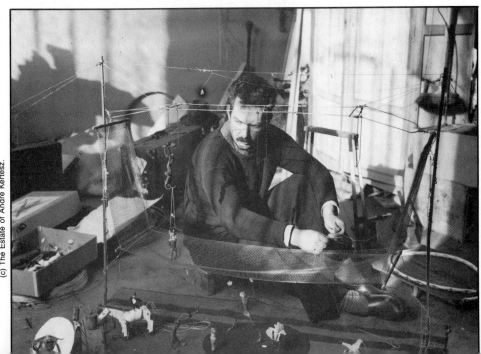

Calder sat on the floor next to the ring. He made the sounds for the seals and lions. He made all the animals and people move to the tune of the circus.

There was a dog that could sit up and even jump through a paper ring. Two seals tossed a ball again and again from one nose to another. There was a man who could pick up something heavy and hold it over his head. There was a woman singing tunes. There was someone who could spring onto the back of a pony.

When people watched Calder's circus, they had fun. Smiles bloomed on every face in the room. The people felt Calder's love of the circus.

Calder's work on paper showed his love of play. One learns that his painting has the feeling of his other work.

First, Calder would put the paper down flat. Next, he soaked it with water. He let the paper dry a little. Then, he began to paint. Sometimes Calder would use paint right from the can. He didn't always mix it. He would paint anything that came to mind. He gave each painting a life of its own. He covered a big sheet of paper with the sun, a face, or a bug.

Calder wanted his art to have life. He wanted his art to move. He makes you think of things in life that move. A little wind makes Calder's work move about. Fish swim. Birds fly. Flowers bloom. Leaves sail in the wind. It takes time to see all that follows.

As a boy, Calder would listen to the song of the wind. He would listen to the sounds of little birds. When one listens these sounds please the ears. It seems as though Calder wanted to please the eyes, as well, with things that move.

Seeing Calder's art makes you want to touch it. You want to move it a little with your fingers. It's as though you want to play, too— "just for the fun of it."

If your fingers could touch it, you would feel the love of life that lives in Calder's art.

Thinking and Writing About the Selection

1. Name some of the animals that Calder made.

2. What sounds would Calder listen to at the circus?

3. Do you think that people liked Calder's circus? Why?

 4. Which work of Calder's do you like best? Why do you like it?

Applying the Key Skill
Summarize

Read the two sentences. Choose the sentence below that has the same meaning. Write that sentence on your paper.

Alexander Calder liked to listen to the circus sounds. He could tell by listening to the songs what would happen next.

a. By listening to circus songs Calder could tell what would happen next.

b. Of all the sounds in the circus, Calder liked circus tunes the best.

Through Grandpa's Eyes

Patricia MacLachlan

Illustrated by Deborah Kogan Ray

Grandpa could not see Calder's circus. But Grandpa's eyes have a message for John. They tell him many things. John learns to see through Grandpa's eyes.

Of all the houses that I know, I like my grandpa's best. There are other fine houses. But Grandpa's house is the one I like most. Because I see it through Grandpa's eyes.

Grandpa is blind. He doesn't see the house the way I do. He sees in his own way. In the morning, the sun pushes through the shades into my eyes. I slide down under the covers to get away, but the light follows me. I give up, kick off the covers, and run to Grandpa's room.

The sun wakes Grandpa in another way. He says it touches him, warming him awake. When I peek in Grandpa's door, he is up. He smiles because he hears me.

"Good day, John."

"Where's Nana?" I ask him.

"Don't you know?" he says. "Close your eyes, John, and look through my eyes." I close my eyes and listen.

"Nana is making breakfast," I say. When I open my eyes, I see Grandpa looking at me.

Grandpa's eyes are sharp blue, even though they are not sharp seeing.

"Breakfast!" calls Nana. "I smell eggs and toast with jam," says Grandpa. He leans his head close to mine.

The wood railing on the steps shows a path where Grandpa has run his fingers up and down. I walk down the steps, too, my fingers following Grandpa's path.

We go in to eat breakfast. Nana hands us each a plate of food. As Grandpa begins to eat, his plate of food is a clock.

"Two eggs at nine o'clock and toast at two o'clock," says Nana to Grandpa.

"A drop of jam," I tell Grandpa, "at six o'clock."

I make my plate of food a clock, too, and eat through Grandpa's eyes.

After breakfast, I follow Grandpa's path to another room. He takes his cello.

"Will you play with me, John?" he asks.

"Listen," says Grandpa. "I will play a song I learned when I was your age. It was the song I liked best."

He plays the tune while I listen. That is the way Grandpa learns new tunes. By listening. "Now," says Grandpa, "the two of us can try it. That's fine," says Grandpa as we play.

Grandpa and I walk outside, to the front yard. We walk to the water. Grandpa was not blind all his life. He remembers in his mind the gleam of the sun on the water.

"I feel a south wind," says Grandpa.

I can tell which way the wind goes because I see the way the tops of the trees lean. Grandpa tells by the way the wind feels on his face.

When we come to the water, I see a blackbird with a red patch. It is on a cattail.

"What is that bird over there, Grandpa?"

"Conk-a-ree," the bird calls to us.

"A red-winged blackbird," says Grandpa.

He can't see where the bird is, but he hears the song of the bird.

As we walk back to the house, Grandpa stops suddenly. He leans his head and listens. He looks to the sky. "Honkers," he whispers.

I look up and see a flock of geese, flying in a V.

We walk up the path again and to the yard where Nana is painting some chairs. Grandpa smells the paint.

"What color, Nana?" he says. "I can't smell the color."

"Blue," I tell him. "Blue like the sky."

"Blue like the color of Grandpa's eyes," Nana says.

Late in the day, Grandpa, Nana, and I take some books outside to read under a tree. Grandpa reads his book with his fingers, feeling the Braille dots that tell him the words. As he reads, Grandpa laughs out loud.

"Tell us what the joke is," says Nana. "Read to us, Papa."

Grandpa does.

When dinner is over, Grandpa puts on the TV. I watch, but Grandpa listens. The sounds and the words tell him when something is happy or sad.

Somehow, Grandpa knows when it is dark, and he takes me up the steps and tucks me into bed. He leans down to kiss me, his hands feeling my head. "You need a haircut, John," he says.

Before Grandpa leaves, he tugs the light chain over my bed to turn off the light. He does not know it but he's put it on. I lie for a while until he's gone, before I get up to turn off the light.

Then, when it is dark for me the way it is dark for Grandpa, I hear the night sounds that Grandpa hears. The house creaking, the birds singing their last songs of the day, the wind playing with the trees outside.

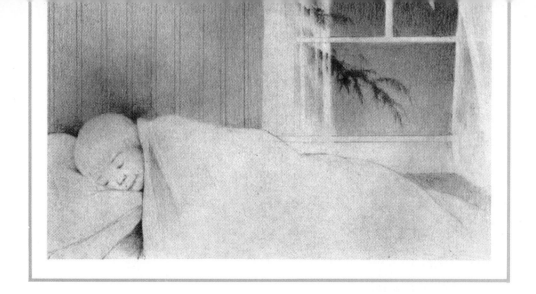

Then, suddenly, I hear the sounds of geese overhead. They fly over the house.

"Grandpa," I whisper. I hope he's heard them, too.

"Honkers," he calls back.

"Go to sleep, John," says Nana.

Grandpa says her voice smiles to him.

"What?" I call to her.

"I said go to sleep," she answers.

She says it sternly. But Grandpa is right. Her voice smiles to me. I know. Because I am looking through Grandpa's eyes.

Thinking and Writing About the Selection

1. How does the sun wake up John?
2. How does the sun wake up Grandpa?
3. Why is Grandpa's plate of food a clock?
4. What other senses help Grandpa to "see"? How?

Applying the Key Skill
Sequence of Events

The sentences below tell what happened in the story "Through Grandpa's Eyes." Write the sentences in the right order.

Last, Grandpa and John walk outside to the water.

Then, Nana calls John and Grandpa to breakfast.

First, the sun wakes John and Grandpa up.

After breakfast, Grandpa plays the cello.

So Will I

My grandfather remembers long ago
the white Queen Anne's lace that grew wild.
He remembers the buttercups and goldenrod
from when he was a child.

He remembers long ago
the white snow falling falling.
He remembers the bluebird and thrush
at twilight
calling, calling.

He remembers long ago
the new moon in the summer sky.
He remembers the wind in the trees
and its long, rising sigh.
And so will I

        so will I.

Charlotte Zolotow

Many Messages

In these stories you read about finding a message in a secret code, a book, a letter, or the tail of a kite. But messages do not always have words—a smile has a special message, too. Messages help to bring friends closer together.

Thinking and Writing About *Many Messages*

1. How did Owl and Caterpillar help to change Bets' mind about reading? How did reading help Tim in "The Code Toad"?

2. In what stories did two people who didn't know each other at the beginning of the story make friends?

3. How did messages help the characters and animals in "Best Wishes, Ed" and "I Wish I Were Back Home"?

4. What might Grandpa in "Through Grandpa's Eyes" have remembered seeing before he was blind?

 5. Write a paragraph that tells why "Many Messages" is a good name for this unit.

136

Glossary

This glossary can help you find out the meaning of words in this book that you may not know.

The words are listed in alphabetical order. Guide words at the top of each page tell you the first and last word on the page. Each word is divided into syllables.

The definitions are adapted from the Macmillan *Beginning Dictionary*.

A

a·bout In regard to; of; concerning. That book is <u>about</u> Ben Franklin.

a·cross From one side to the other; on or to the other side. A bridge <u>across</u> the water led from one city to the other.

act One of the parts of a play; something that is done; to do something or move; to perform in a play. The first <u>act</u> of the play takes place in a castle.

af·ter Following the time that; later; in the rear; behind. <u>After</u> I go to bed, I go to sleep.

af·ter·noon The part of the day between noon and evening. The children will come home from school in the <u>afternoon</u>.

age The amount of time that a person, animal, or thing has lived or existed. Ann will soon be nine years of <u>age</u>.

a·lone Not near or with another or others. When the children went to school, their mother was <u>alone</u> in the house.

al·ways All the time; every time. Do you <u>always</u> look before you cross the street?

an·gry Feeling or showing anger. We were scared when the man spoke in an <u>angry</u> voice.

an·swers Writes or speaks in reply to something. Ted always gives <u>answers</u> when people ask him things.

an·y·more At the present; from now on. When I get tired, I can't work <u>anymore</u>.

an·y·one Any person whatever; anybody. "Does <u>anyone</u> want to come with me to the park?" Mother asked the children.

a·round In a circle and back; along the outer edge of; on all sides of; so as to surround. The children ran from the front door <u>around</u> the house and back again.

art Painting, drawing, and sculpture, or anything that has beauty or meaning. Painting and music are two kinds of <u>art</u>.

a·sleep Sleeping. Mother said, "Don't wake the baby when she is <u>asleep</u>."

B

be·fore Previous to the time when; in front of; ahead of. You should look up and down the street <u>before</u> you cross it.

be·gins Starts; does the first part of something. When it <u>begins</u> to grow dark, the children go home.

best Of the highest quality; superior to all others; in the most successful way; something of the highest quality or excellence. Pam has many friends, but Jill is her <u>best</u> friend.

black·bird Any of various birds that are mostly black. A <u>blackbird</u> has dark feathers.

blue The color of the clear sky in the daytime; having the color blue. Joanne likes <u>blue</u> better than any other color.

box·es Containers used to hold things. We carried home two <u>boxes</u>. One box had dog food, the other had cat food.

braids Strips made by weaving together three or more long pieces of hair, straw, or cloth. Beth didn't want a haircut. She wanted to keep her long <u>braids</u>.

break·fast The first meal of the day. Many people have toast, eggs, and something to drink for <u>breakfast</u>.

bring To cause something or someone to come with you; to cause something to come or happen. Ted asked Jane to <u>bring</u> her sister with her when she came to his house.

broth·er A boy or man having the same parents as another person. Amanda's <u>brother</u>, Jack, is the only boy in the family.

C

Cal·der, Al·ex·an·der An American artist. The art of <u>Alexander Calder</u> has a message for many people.

card A flat piece of stiff paper that may have words, numbers, or some kind of design on it. If you have a library <u>card</u> you can take books out of the library.

car·ried Held something while moving it. Jerry <u>carried</u> his books to school.

cart·wheel A kind of jump from one's feet to one's hands and back again. You use your hands and feet to turn a <u>cartwheel</u>.

cas·tle A large building or group of buildings having high thick walls with towers. The king and queen lived in the <u>castle</u>.

cat·tail A tall plant that grows in marshes. Do you know how the top of a <u>cattail</u> feels?

cel·lo A musical instrument that is like a violin but larger and lower in tone. A <u>cello</u> is a kind of box with strings that is played to make music.

child A son or daughter; a young boy or girl. The little <u>child</u> cried and asked for its mother and father.

cir·cus A show with trained animals and acrobats, clowns, and other people who do special things. A <u>circus</u> is a show put on by people and animals in a big tent.

code Any set of signals, words, or symbols used to send messages. You can use a <u>code</u> to write a secret message.

col·lec·tion A gathering together. Miles has a huge <u>collection</u> of games that he likes to play.

col·or Red, blue, or yellow. All the other colors are a combination or shade of red, blue, or yellow; to give color to. The <u>color</u> red is sometimes a sign for "stop," "hot," or "on."

com·put·ers Electronic machines that can solve difficult mathematical and logical problems at very high speeds. People use <u>computers</u> to help them with work at school and on the job.

cov·ered Put something over or on; hidden or protected. Snow <u>covered</u> the houses, the trees, and the ground.

D

dark Having little or no light. It is <u>dark</u> at night, even when the moon is out.

daught·er A female child. Father and Mother's first child was a <u>daughter</u>. They named her Mary.

dear Much or greatly loved. Ben wrote, "<u>Dear</u> Andy," as he began his letter.

di·rec·tions Orders or instructions on how to do something or how to act; the lines or courses along which something moves, faces, or lies. If you want something you make to turn out well, you should follow the <u>directions</u>.

drag·on An imaginary beast that is supposed to look something like a giant lizard with claws and wings. A <u>dragon</u> is a huge animal that people have made up.

E

end To bring or come to an end; the last part. Jerry watched the show to the <u>end</u> and went to bed when it was over.

e·ven Still; yet; even though it may seem unlikely. Meg is still my friend, <u>even</u> though I am angry with her.

F

feath·ers The light growths that cover a bird's skin. A bird's <u>feathers</u> are like a coat for the bird.

felt Touched; found about by touching or handling; thought or believed. Mona <u>felt</u> the water to see if it was hot.

fin·gers The five separate parts at the end of the hand. People use their <u>fingers</u> to do many things.

flew Moved through the air. The bird <u>flew</u> from the tree to its nest on the porch.

fol·low To go or come after; to act according to; to go along. Leo will <u>follow</u> the rabbit's tracks to find out where it went.

G

gold A heavy yellow metal used to make jewelry and coins. The pretty necklace was made of gold.

gone Moved from one place to another. The bus had gone by the time Nan got to the bus stop, so she had to wait for the next one.

guess To form an opinion without having enough knowledge or facts to be sure; to get the correct answer by guessing; to think, believe, or suppose. Can you guess how many books are in the library?

H

hair·cut The act or style of cutting the hair. Mother gave Emily a haircut and cut off her braids.

hap·pen To take place; occur; occur by chance. What do you think will happen if you water the seeds in the ground?

hard Needing or using much effort; solid and firm to the touch, not soft. Sam finds it hard to do all the things he wants to in one day.

has To have. Peter has a new baby brother.

hat·ed Disliked very much. The little boy hated having a haircut.

heav·y Having great weight. It was hard to move the heavy boxes.

hers The one or ones that belong to or relate to her. Scott reads his book, and Gloria reads hers.

honkers A word that is sometimes used for geese. Honkers are birds with a cry that sounds like a horn.

I

ice·berg A very large piece of floating ice. Penguins were living on the iceberg.

I'll Contraction for "I will" and "I shall." "I'll help you with those books," said the librarian.

inch·es Measures of length that equals 1/12 of a foot. Do you know how many inches there are in a foot?

in·for·ma·tion Knowledge or facts about something. Ted wants to find information about where bears live.

in·side On, in, or towards the inside; within. Jeff found out what was inside the box when he opened it.

is·land A body of land that is completely surrounded by water. An island has water all around it.

J

job A position of work; employment; something that has to be done. Father works in Newport, where he has a job painting signs.

K

king A man who rules a country. The king had a huge kingdom to look after.

king·dom A country that is ruled by a king or queen. A trip through the kingdom took a very long time.

L

let·ter A written message; a mark that stands for a speech sound. Ed wrote Kate a letter to tell her about his trip.

Dear Kate,
My trip to Canada was lots of fun! I wish you could have been there too! I miss you.
Your friend,
Ed

li·brar·i·an A person who is in charge of a library. A <u>librarian</u> can help you find books in a library.

li·brar·y A collection of books and magazines. Jeff found a good book to read in the <u>library</u>.

lis·tened Tried to hear; paid attention in order to hear. Sue <u>listened</u> as her father spoke.

M

mag·a·zines A printed collection of stories, articles, and pictures, usually bound in a paper cover. Most libraries have <u>magazines</u>, as well as books, to read.

man·y Made up of a large number; a large number. <u>Many</u> people live in a big city.

me·di·a cen·ter A <u>media center</u> is a room that may have books, records, games, and computers.

mes·sage Words sent from one person to another. "If you will write your <u>message</u> on this paper, I will give it to my mother," said Sue.

mes·sen·ger A person who delivers messages or runs errands. The <u>messenger</u> arrived with a package for Tim.

mill·er A person who owns or operates a mill for grinding grain. We make bread with what the <u>miller</u> ground.

mon·ey The coins and paper currency of a country. Gloria saved her <u>money</u> to pay for the new skates.

morn·ing The first part of the day, which ends at noon. We get up in the <u>morning</u> and eat breakfast.

most Greatest in number, amount, or degree; nearly all. Some of the girls are reading, but <u>most</u> of them are playing a game.

move To change the place or direction of something; to put into motion. Dan helped his mother move the chair from the room to the porch.

mu·sic A pleasing or beautiful combination of sounds. Music is made up of many sounds that please the ear.

must Should; have to; need to. We must return the books that we borrow from the library.

N

neck·lace A string of beads or other piece of jewelry worn around the neck for decoration. Mother took the necklace and put it on over her head.

New York City The largest city in the United States. Many people visit New York City.

New·port A city in Rhode Island. Carlos lived in Newport.

news·pa·pers Printed sheets of paper that contain news, interest stories, opinions on local and national happenings, and advertising. My mother reads two newspapers every day.

noise A sound that is loud and harsh. The people at the game yelled and shouted and made a lot of noise.

no·tice To become aware of; observe. Did you notice the new stop sign?

num·ber The total amount of things in a group; how many there are of something. Tell me the <u>number</u> of children in this room.

O

old Having lived or existed for a long period of time. Mr. Bloom has many <u>old</u> coins in his collection that date back to the early 1800s.

oth·er Different from the one or ones already mentioned; not the same. Jason and the <u>other</u> boys were playing soccer.

our Of or belonging to us. Emily and I feed <u>our</u> pets.

P

paint A mixture of coloring matter and water, oil, or some other liquid; to cover with paint. We will use green <u>paint</u> to <u>paint</u> the roof.

pa·per A material that is used for writing, printing, wrapping things, covering walls, and many other purposes; a piece of paper. The girls made a kite out of <u>paper</u>, string, sticks, and <u>glue</u>.

patch A small area that is different from what is around it. The pony had a <u>patch</u> of white on its back.

Patz·cua·ro, Mex·i·co A city in Mexico which is on a lake. Alba lives in <u>Patzcuaro</u>, <u>Mexico</u>.

pen·cils Long, thin tools for writing or drawing, usually made of sticks of graphite enclosed in a covering of wood. The children wrote on their paper with <u>pencils</u>.

pen·guins Seabirds whose feathers are black or gray on the back and white on the chest. <u>Penguins</u> are large birds that can't fly. They live in places where there is ice and snow.

pic·ture A painting, drawing, or photograph that represents a person or thing. Kate will draw a <u>picture</u> of what she thinks a dragon looks like.

poor Having little money; bad. Freddy was <u>poor</u> because he had no money.

porch A roofed area built onto a house. Jeff sat on the <u>porch</u> at the front of his house and looked up and down the street.

pub·lic Having to do with or for all the people. Our city has a <u>public</u> library and a <u>public</u> school.

Q

queen A woman who rules a kingdom. The <u>queen</u> gave the poor man some gold.

R

rec·ords A written account of something; a disk on which music or other sounds have been recorded to be played back on a phonograph. Sally likes to listen to <u>records</u> with singing.

red-winged Having red wings. A <u>red-winged</u> blackbird has a patch of red feathers in two places.

re·mem·bers Brings back or recalls to the mind. At first Jim doesn't know where his coat is, then he <u>remembers</u> he left it at school.

re·port An account or statement about something; to make or give a report; to present oneself. Mr. Raymond and Mr. Pompey report for work at eight o'clock.

rest Something that is left; remainder; others; to stop work or activity. We go to school from eight until three o'clock, then for the rest of the day we play.

Ringling Brothers Barnum and Bailey Circus A circus started in the early 1900s which became the most famous circus in America. We went to see the Ringling Brothers Barnum and Bailey Circus.

S

sec·ond Next after the first; below the first or best; another. "My second name is Anne," said Betty Anne, "but most people just call me Betty."

sharp Having an edge or point that cuts easily; not rounded. A cat has sharp claws and can scratch.

side·ways Toward or from one side. Meg asked Tom to face front and step right to move sideways.

sing·ing Making words or sound with musical tones. The children are singing a song that they wrote.

smil·ing Having or giving an expression of the face made by turning up the corners of the mouth. Jenny was smiling and laughing because she was happy.

song A piece of music that is sung. A song is made up of words and music.

sounds Noises; things that can be heard. Nan heard cracking and creaking <u>sounds</u> when she was alone in the house.

south The direction to your left as you watch the sun set in the evening; toward or in the south. A <u>south</u> wind comes from the direction <u>south</u>.

spend To pay out money; to pass time; to use up. Father had to <u>spend</u> a lot of money to fix the car.

spin·ning wheel A large wheel and a spindle on a stand. What does the woman spin on the <u>spinning wheel</u>?

splash·es Sounds made by something hitting water or another liquid; throws water or another liquid about. The <u>splashes</u> of the fish made us all wet.

stern·ly In a harsh or strict way. Father was angry, and he spoke <u>sternly</u> to the children.

straw The dry stalks of grains after they have been cut and threshed. The pony had a bed of <u>straw</u>.

street A public way in a town or city. The cars going down the <u>street</u> will stop at the red light.

string A thin line of twisted threads or wire. Betty tied one end of the <u>string</u> to the kite. She will hold the other end in her hand.

swam Moved about in the water by using arms or legs, or fins and tail. Jan <u>swam</u> to the boat and got in it.

T

ta·bles Pieces of furniture with flat tops supported by one or more legs. There were so many people for dinner that we needed two tables.

teach·er A person who gives lessons or classes. The teacher asked many questions about the story.

third Next after second; one of three equal parts. The first pencil is blue, the second is red, and the third is green.

though In spite of the fact that; but; yet; however. Though Ed got up at six o'clock, he was late for school.

through From one end or side to the other; to various parts or places in; by means of. The dog ran through the house, from one room to another.

tie To fasten or attach with a bow or knot. We will use string to tie the box.

toast Sliced bread that has been browned by heat. Julian likes to eat toast and jam.

told Put into words; said. Jack read a book that told about elephants.

touch·es Puts the hand on or against something. Pat touches the feathers with his fingers to learn how they feel.

tried Made an effort to do something. When Cindy tried to turn a cartwheel, she found that she could.

true Agreeing with the facts; not false, wrong, or made-up. It is true that owls have feathers.

tune A series of notes that make up a song or the melody of a piece of music. The old man remembered a tune he had heard long ago.

turn To move or cause to move around in a circle or part of a circle; to go or make go a certain or different way. If you turn around, you will see what is in back of you.

TV Television. John watched a news report on TV.

U

un·til Up to the time of; before. Jose stayed up reading <u>until</u> nine o'clock.

W

wave To move freely back and forth or up and down; to show or signal by waving the hand; a rippling movement on the surface of water. Greg and Kim <u>wave</u> to the people on the bus.

whale A large animal that has a body like a fish. A <u>whale</u> is not a fish, but it lives in the water.

which What one or ones; any one or ones. <u>Which</u> color do you like better, blue or red?

whole Having all its parts; entire; complete. The <u>whole</u> family will take a trip. No one will stay home.

wrote Formed the letters, words, or symbols of something on paper or some other surface. Oliver <u>wrote</u> a letter and put it in the mail.

Y

yard An area of ground next to or surrounding a house, There is a big <u>yard</u> around the house where the children play.

yell To cry out loudly. "I can hear you very well," said Nan. "You don't have to <u>yell</u> so loud."